Endurance Publications Inc.

educational entertainment for kids on the go!

Endurance Publications
POB 101 Agoura Hills, CA 91376

This book is available at a special discount when ordered in bulk quantities.
For information: fax 916 482 7450
www.endurancepublications.com

ISBN 0-9708805-0-2

Copyright 2001 Jeff Lappin
Illustrations by Jeremy Madl
Edited by Suzanne Wolf, Kathy Byrd, and Sabra Chili
Graphic Design by Azar Jahangiri

Printed in China by Palace Press International/ Sabra Chili
Library of Congress Control Number: 20001117276

1 2 3 4 5 6 7 8 9 0

A special thanks to Azar Jahangiri, Marc and Lisa Sallin, Mom and Dad and every child in the world that enjoys this book.
Thank you all!!

When I get older,
I want to ride my bike
around the world.

What do you see on the mobile?

I can sit up now. I think this is the position you're in when you ride your bike.

How many fingers do you count on the handle-bars?

Every time I stand up, my
legs are getting stronger
and soon I will be able to
ride a bike.

What color is my jacket? Why are my pants rolled up?

I ride around in my walker, going from room to room. I'm practicing my pedaling. Sometimes, I run over my dad's feet.

Do you remember riding in your walker?

I'm walking now, but I fall down sometimes. I can't wait until I can ride a bike all by myself.

What is behind me on the ground? What color are the houses?

I sit behind my dad on his bike and he takes me around the block almost everyday.

Have you ever gone really fast? What was it like?

Every time I go to the market with my mom, I sit on the ride in the front of the store. But, I know it's not the real thing.

What different rides have you been on?

My dad bought me my
first big wheel. I ride it up
and down the driveway
all day long.

Do you remember riding your Big Wheel?

I go so fast now. I ride from the beginning of the driveway into the backyard.

What's in my backyard?

It's my birthday today and my parents bought me a real bicycle with training wheels.

I finally have a dirt bike with training wheels. This is the best day of my life!

The training wheels help me so I don't fall down.

On my new bike, I go faster than ever. Sometimes I pretend I'm in a race.

Where am I riding?

You have to be extra careful on your bike. Watch out for cars and always wear the right equipment.

What color are the bicycle helmets?

My dad thinks I'm ready to take my training wheels off. But he follows me to make sure I don't fall down.

Do you remember the first time you rode your bike?

Sometimes I follow my mom and dad and we ride all the way around the block. My mom has a road bike and my dad has a mountain bike.

How many street lights do you see?

Now that I am a little older,
I have my own business.
I'm saving up for a
mountain bike.

What kind of business do I have? What other goodies can I sell?

With the help of my mom and dad, I finally saved up enough money for my new mountain bike.

Do you have a pet fish? What's it's name?

It's Saturday and my mom and dad are taking me to the park to have a picnic and ride my new bike.

Can you guess what's in the picnic basket?

In the back of the park, there is a single track that leads into the mountains. It's a perfect trail for my new bike.

Riding your bike in the mountains is the coolest thing to do.

See you on the trails!

How many rocks am I riding past?

Marcel's Biking Tips

Having the right size bike is very important so you can have complete control.

Having the right type of bike is very important depending on the conditions that you will be riding in. For example, you wouldn't want to ride a Road Bike in the mountains.

Always make sure that you have the proper equipment when riding your bike. At the very least, a helmet! It's the law.

Always be aware of your surroundings when riding your bike. Make sure the conditions are safe. For example, a rocky track or too many cars can be dangerous.

Always look two or three times when crossing a street and always use a crosswalk when one is available.

Be courteous. Use the designated trails for riding and slow down for hikers and horses.

Never litter. Always take your trash home.

Marcel's Biking Glossary

Big Wheel A small plastic tricycle with a big front wheel.

Training Wheels Small wheels that attach to the back wheel of your bike to help keep you from falling down.

Dirt Bike An all around type of bike that is best used for riding in the dirt. Example: BMX Bike.

Equipment Helmet, gloves, proper shoes and attire, sunglasses.

Road Bike A type of bike used only for riding on streets.

Mountain Bike A type of bike used for riding in the mountains

Single Track A trail in the mountains that is specifically designed for riding your Mountain Bike.